NOTHING STAYS THE SAME
~but that's okay~

written + illustrated by
SARA OLSHER

mighty ·AND· bright ™

helping families handle hard things

We love to see pictures of you with your book!
Tag us @mightyandbrightco on Instagram.

Hi, my name is Mia!

And this is **Stuart.**
Stuart feels better when he knows
what's going to happen every day.

(Actually, *everyone* feels better when they know
what's going to happen—even grown-ups!)

Most of the time,
we do the same things in the mornings.
We wake up.

We eat breakfast.
(I like apples. Stuart only eats **bugs**.)

Usually our nights are the same, too.
We brush our teeth.

We put on our jammies, and we go to bed.
Every day ends with sleep.

But our days can be different.
Some days we go to school, and some days are the weekend!

We can see the different days on a calendar like this one.
When something goes from one thing to being a different thing,
it's called a **change**.

Our changes are on the calendar!

MONDAY   TUESDAY   WEDNESDAY   T

Sometimes we get to choose our changes, like our opinion about the best ice cream flavor.

Small changes happen every day.
Every day the weather changes and we have to
figure out what clothes to wear.
Our feelings change - sometimes we are
happy, and sometimes we are sad.

Then there's bigger changes, like
starting a new school,
having a friend move away,
meeting new people,
getting a pet,
becoming a big brother or sister . . .

moving to a n

someone

a new sport, one of

weather getting war

a new babysitt

new teache

having

losi

This is kind of scary.

When something big changes,
what we do each day can change too.

Stuart wants to know,
what if something big changes?

Will I be okay?
The answer is a **big YES!**
You will be okay.

Even though everything might **feel** different, a lot stays the same.

If you move to a new house, you might wake up in a different place. But you still go to sleep at night, and you still wake up in the morning.

Change can be hard for a while.
Stuart's not sure what to *do* now that things are different.

Will there be new people?
Will there be new things to do each day?

It takes awhile to learn a new way of doing things.

When you don't know what will happen each day,
changes can be extra hard. Our brains need time to get ready!

We can use a calendar to see what changes will come
and what will stay the same.

MONDAY   TUESDAY   WEDNESDAY   THURSDAY   FRIDAY   SATURDAY   SUNDAY

If our friend is going to move away, we can see
on our calendar when we will see them again!

After a while, *we all get used to change* and it doesn't feel new anymore - it just feels like our normal life.

But our brains need some time to get used to big changes.
While we are playing
or sleeping
or eating
or teaching a cat to hulahoop
... our brains are very busy thinking about lots of things!

Sometimes our brains are doing **too much**.

A too-busy brain can make us feel really **big** feelings
and *we don't know why*. We might start to cry or feel angry.
We might also get a tight chest, a tummy ache, or a headache.

It's important to be kind to our brains, and remember to help them!
There are lots of activities that help a too-busy brain.

Lots of kids have worries when something changes.
But no matter what, you will always be loved.

Even if **beetles riding meatballs** rained from the sky.

Weeee!

Even if you *ate* a beetle riding a meatball (ew).
There's **nothing** you can do to make your grown-ups stop loving you.

Kids have a lot of questions, and it's important to get answers!
So don't worry! Go ahead and ask the
weirdest questions on the planet.

what if my new school is on a boat in the middle of the ocean and my teacher is a purple and orange dinosaur that eats dolphins for lunch and speaks a weird language nobody has ever heard before and I am the only kid and I don't <u>want</u> to eat a dolphin? **WHAT THEN?**

Even though some things are changing, lots of things will stay the same.
Every morning you will wake up, and every night, you'll go to sleep.

And there will always be **lots** of grown-ups who care and want to help you.

...and so many more.

Stuart feels a lot better now that he knows what to expect.
Even though our days can be different, it helps to plan out
our week so we know what's going to happen next,
and remember that we are safe and loved.

There are lots of fun things to look forward to, like movies, sports, play
dates, craft time, and special time with people we love.

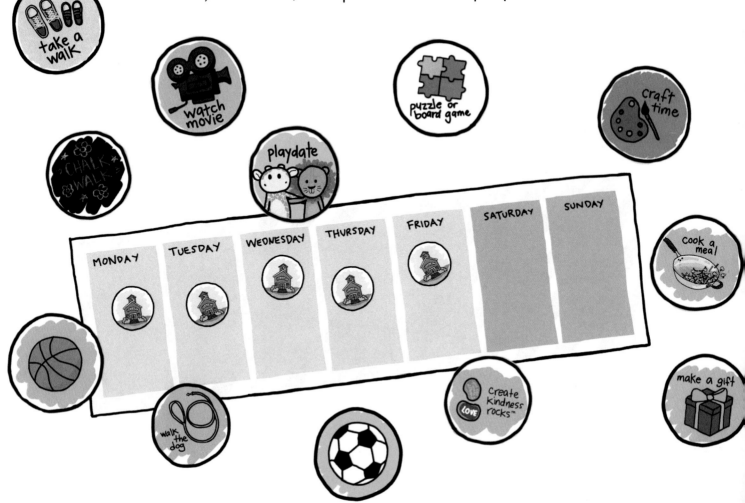

And remember, when things get hard, it's important to share how you are feeling with a grown-up.

We can do hard things — together!

Hi! My name is Sara, and I write + illustrate kids' books.

Things I LOVE!

- reading
- Dancing (Badly)
- my family
- animals
- Quiet time
- Rainbows
- candy
- nature

I live in a state known for trees + rain, in a city nicknamed "the cherry city."

I do all my drawings on an iPad with an Apple pencil

I live with my daughter and our cats, Tater, Waffle + Batman. One day, I want a goat, and I want to name him CAULIFLOWER!

?!

Hey Parents!

You don't have to be a superhero to be an *incredible* parent.

There's no shortage of parenting information out there.
But most of us feel like we can barely make it through the day
... let alone thoughtfully develop the skills our kids need.

At Mighty + Bright, we've figured out how to:

- Incorporate emotional + mental wellbeing into your day-to-day life

- Learn a common language with your kids

- Make your parenting life easier

- Reduce meltdowns and underlying anxiety

      ...with no thick parenting books,
      (and no digital parenting courses.)

Find more books like this
and tools that'll totally
change your family

SCAN THIS USING YOUR PHONE
or visit: mightyandbright.com/emotions

We believe it shouldn't take *more* effort to guide your kids the way you want to guide them.
It just takes a different perspective.

Book Sara for school visits and
public speaking at saraolsher.com

mighty -AND- bright™

helping families handle hard things

Published by Mighty + Bright
mightyandbright.com

ISBN: 978-1-7366114-2-5

want to tell
Sara something?
Send a letter!

Sara Olsher
13203 SE 172ND Ave
Suite 166, #1121
Happy Valley, Oregon
97086

Made in the USA
Coppell, TX
04 October 2023

22394572R10021